# A Guide to Training in General Practice

) S S

Freelance Consultant and Trainer

# About the Author

Fran Ross is a freelance consultant and trainer working with individuals and teams to develop and enhance personal, professional and business relationships. She has worked within a university and the NHS as a consultant and trainer for 10 years. She was the first winner of the NHS Training Division's 'Trainer of the Year' award in 1993/94. She is also a Master NLP Practitioner and applies this learning to all areas of her work, and is a member of the Institute of Personnel and Development. Fran lives on a barge with her husband John in an idyllic setting within a nature reserve on the River Hamble.

*First Published 1997*
*Reprinted 1998*

*Printed by Redhouse Press Ltd*
*Dartford, Kent*

**ISBN**

1 873839 25 1

Further copies of *A guide to training in general practice* may be obtained from Pi books, a division of Publishing Initiatives (Europe) Ltd. This publication reflects the view and experience of the author and not necessarily those of Publishing Initiatives (Europe) Ltd.

# Contents

# CONTENTS

# Introduction

**N**ever has there been a time in the history of general practice when it has been so important to give attention to the people who work within it.

The past six years have seen rapid change as a direct result of the 1990 GMS contract that constitutes the terms and conditions of service for GPs. The NHS reforms stemming from *Working for Patients* (1989) have seen the focus of care shift from secondary to primary care. GP fundholding has been the catalyst for the speed of these changes. To keep pace with these changes, GPs (some for the first time) have had to examine their role as employers. Part of this role has meant a responsibility to employ people who can work to their full capacity and capability to deliver care to meet today's standards. This means making an investment in the people they employ in terms of their training and development. It also means that GPs need to review their own training and educational needs to match the continuing development of primary care.

Any employer or manager of people has a responsibility to identify and meet training needs, as well as evaluating the effectiveness of the training delivered. Organisations do not survive without people who are confident and competent in what they do. Where is this more important than in organisations that deliver health care to patients? If the trust people have in their professional health care is to be upheld, investment in the people who work within it has never been more important.

The purpose of this book is to guide you through some choices available to help your team to develop to its full effectiveness, and the individuals within the team to reach their full potential.

As you hold this book in your hands, you may be considering organising some training and learning in your practice. You may also be considering your own role as a trainer, facilitator or co-ordinator for the team. You may be weighing up the costs and benefits, or it may just be an idea floating around in your head. More pragmatically, you may have noticed that sending staff out for training can be expensive, and that the benefits of this training for the team may not always be tangible. Also, the cost of staff replacement and the stress placed on those left behind to complete the work can be too high. You may be considering what options are available to change the situation. You may also be aware that the practice has not had a training strategy for the team before. You may have this nagging feeling that this is something that could be happening for the benefit of the team members, the practice and, ultimately, the patients.

This book is designed to assist you and the practice team to make some new choices. This may lead to you and the team learning together, which will in turn reinforce the team spirit. The practice culture should gain higher levels of trust, understanding, knowledge and skills, and these benefits will be passed to the patients registered with the practice.

# Chapter One

## Making a start

# Making a start

## Managing the change

J ust like any other change, the training strategy will need planning. If it is likely that you will be the person to take these ideas forward, you could begin very easily by giving yourself a bit of thinking time with a pencil and paper.

Begin by asking yourself whether this has been tried before. The fact that you have this book suggests that you have started gathering information that has been published on the subject. A useful addition to this would be a personal account from another practice that seems to be successful at training and learning together. If no such practice springs to mind, you could give the Training Department at your Health Authority a call; they usually know who the innovators are and can put you in touch with such a practice that would be willing to talk to you. At the same time, you can inform the Health Authority about what you want to do; they may be impressed and willing to support you with much more information. You may gain access to their resources, including any funding that may be available. Why not go and see the people who have the lead on primary-care development - you may discover that you have mutual aims.

### Is the time right for change?

Take a moment to think about the practice as a whole:

- What is the current level of activity?
- What is in the pipeline in addition to the normal day-to-day service delivery?
- Are you building an extension?
- Are you moving to new premises?
- Are you about to start fundholding?

If you are involved in other big changes, then there will not be much in the way of 'slack resources'. This is a jargon term used to describe the space and time people will need to give any new change the attention required for it to be successful. If there is not much 'slack' in the practice system, then you might want to put this idea on hold until the timing is better.

## Using a domainal map

The next question to ask is who needs to make the decision with you if these ideas are to go ahead. Who are the key people who will be affected by this decision? To help you do this you could try using a management tool called a domainal map (Appendix 1).

This is a tool taken from industry, and is tried and tested in managing change in general practice[1]. Begin by making a list of the key people or 'stakeholders'. This might include: the partners; the GP trainee; the team nurses, both in-house and attached; the administration staff; the practice manager; and any other people involved, such as paramedics. A 'stakeholder' is anyone who you think will be affected by the practice having a team training strategy, or who could affect such a strategy should there be one. Don't forget to include yourself in this.

To create the domainal map:

- Start with six concentric circles.

- Divide these six circles into as many segments as there are stakeholders.

- Put the name of your proposed change into the centre circle.

- In the second circle put the names of the stakeholders.

- In the third circle make a note of the current involvement of each stakeholder in training.

- In the fourth describe the future benefits of the change for each stakeholder.

- The fifth circle should contain the potential costs to each individual should a training strategy should go ahead.

- In the outer circle make a note of the unconscious 'wrecking power' of each stakeholder.

To complete the third circle, think about each group or individual you have identified. Focus on each name on your list; if it's a group then think about the group's members - focus so that you include everyone. For example, think about the administration staff; have a picture of them all in your mind's eye or hear what they sound like when they are working. Ask yourself how this group is currently involved in training. How is training organised? Who is responsible for it? Is there a plan for it? Is it working? Make some brief notes on the map.

Repeat this process for each group or individual in the team. When you have gathered this information (it may only take a few minutes do this), you can move to the fourth circle, the future benefits. Ask yourself, for each group or individual, if a team training strategy were to go ahead what would be the benefits to them? Be very specific, as these thoughts will probably influence these people to adopt the idea. For example, some benefits to GPs might be:

- Training needs that relate closely to the practice objectives; better value for training spend.

- A well-trained team may enable them to spend less time on non-clinical matters.

- Opportunity to introduce good human resource practices (appraisals, personal development plans, training plans).

- Proper use by the team of investment in computers.

- More satisfied patients.

Then note in the fifth circle what would be the potential costs to each of the individuals or groups. It is worth taking the time to be very specific, as you are identifying the barriers or blocks that people may have to this idea. For a practice manager these might include:

- Time involvement if s/he is managing the process or providing in-house training.

- Practice plans may identify unwelcome training needs for him/her or others.

If you are clear about what the stakeholders' costs are, then you can begin to think of ways to minimise them.

Lastly, for this exercise, think carefully about what each individual or group could do to wreck this project. This will be important information to have later. The theory is that if you are able to tell people what their wrecking power is, then they are less likely to use it. This theory does not assume that people will act maliciously or with awareness; people will wreck your project unconsciously whilst engaged in their own agenda. Acknowledgement of their agenda and their power to wreck yours is often all that is needed to get them on your side.

Having done this thinking, you will have collected some invaluable data all on one piece of paper. You will also have completed a feasibility study. If the cost of this idea to most of the 'stakeholders' outweighs any benefits they might gain, then it is not likely to be very successful as it stands. If, however, the benefits outweigh the costs for the majority of the stakeholders, then the idea has a good chance of being a winner.

Let's imagine for a moment the benefits a joint team learning strategy may have for, say, a GP trainee. What if there was a training plan for him/her that did not involve just the practice trainer? Imagine the benefits to that individual and to primary care, if the trainee spent time learning practice finance from the practice manager, and health needs assessment from the attached health visitor. What other possibilities are there? Why not add them to your map.

Now let's think about the patients. What would be the benefits to them of a well-trained practice team? It could be that their confidence in the practice's services will grow. When confidence and trust are high, people are more compliant and co-operative. Think what that would mean: more satisfying clinical outcomes; a more effective organisation; more efficient use of NHS funds.

# Sharing the idea with the team

The next step is for you to discuss with individuals and groups your ideas thus far. This could be done informally in corridors or coffee times. You might arrange a slot on any relevant meetings - practice team, practice staff, partnership, whatever applies in your practice. Some useful questions to ask about your proposal might be:

- What appeals to you about this idea?
- What questions would you like answered?
- What concerns you?
- Is this the right time for our practice to be doing this?

The answers will enable you to refine the data on your domainal map, and to be even clearer about the barriers or difficulties people may have. They will also give you a clearer sense of how successful you are likely to be.

People may identify concerns about loss of peer group training as a cost of team training. You will need to make it clear that it will be the team itself that will define its needs, which will mean matching individuals and groups to appropriate training content.

Why not survey the patients for their views about the practice? This will help the practice to define the level of service it needs to offer, and should be a helpful step towards identifying training needs, both in skills and attitudes. A questionnaire sent to a cross-section of patients by post is preferable, even though this has a cost implication. To offer a questionnaire to surgery attenders would obviously miss non-attenders, whose opinions you would not want to lose as a result of a problem they encountered on one of their infrequent visits. The questions would need be tailored to find out, for example:

- What do our patients want us to offer?
- What would they rate as a good quality service?

Ultimately, the only way for practices to be truly successful in today's world is to give, or attempt to give, the service that the public wants.

### Negotiating agreement with the key people

At this point, most people in the practice will be aware of your proposals and have formed an opinion about them. Now is the time to seek agreement to go ahead. You could arrange a meeting with the key people, or their representatives if the whole group would be too large to manage well. If you arrange it at a time when most people can attend, they will notice your efforts to include them, even if it is not possible for them all to attend.

Begin by outlining the decision you want to be jointly made by the end of the meeting. All your careful spadework will allow you to know who supports the idea and who opposes it or has reservations. You will also have all the information you need to answer questions. At the meeting, make sure everyone gets a chance to speak and air their views. If you get an agreement from the majority to go ahead, ask those who are resisting if they will try it out for, say, six or nine months, after which the decision will be reviewed. This is called a conditional decision. It is often impossible to predict all the consequences of a decision; you may well have to experience some results, and then review and make changes if necessary. When people have very different views, it is much easier to reach a consensus if they know that they are only agreeing to a trial run, or to a certain point at which the decision will be reviewed.

## Planning the implementation of the team training strategy

### Setting aims and objectives

Given the go-ahead, it is up to you and the group to identify the aims of the training strategy and to set some clear objectives. These are useful as a way of measuring progress, refining the group's thinking, and making modifications along the way.

The overall aim may be something like:

- To have a training and learning plan in this practice, which recognises the needs of the individuals and the development of the team, and enables the practice to deliver its service to patients with effective and efficient care. (These are my words, the ones your team chooses will be the right ones for you.)

Some objectives might be:

- To agree with the partnership a ring-fenced annual budget to be able to deliver the strategy, including start-up costs.
- To identify the training needs of individuals and groups within the practice.
- To match these needs to appropriate training events, either internally organised or external.
- To be clear about training event outcomes, and how we are going to measure them - what are the indicators that would tell us to what extent we have changed?
- To plan these events, and produce a programme for the year.
- To identify the potential trainers in the practice - our in-house 'experts'.
- To identify potential training resources and materials.
- To review progress early in order to celebrate success and make any necessary modifications.

### Agreeing the next steps

The above objectives help to identify the tasks ahead. It may be that you do not have to take responsibility for them all yourself, so agree the tasks and who is going to do what, before you meet again. It might be a good idea at this point to identify a small group to help steer the project.

It is important to agree a realistic time plan. Some milestones should be set out - these are points at which you can measure progress along the way. If, for any reason, you cannot stick to the time agreed, that is fine. It can be reviewed, as can all other aspects of the plan, but if a time plan is not in place, then you may plan and plan and never get going.

## Funding the training strategy

It will be important to establish with the partnership the level of funding available to finance the team's training. This funding will need to include a practice policy about who can have access to training, and to what level. Any policy would need to be drawn up by representatives of the team. This will help to create ownership of the strategy, and delivery to the practice's identified priorities. The policy needs to include equity of access as far as possible. My experience has been that, whenever funds have been limited for whatever reason, the nursing staff will quickly use up the available funds. This is because the nurses' work is viewed as potentially income-generating. Whilst this is important, it is tough for other team members to be left out. Their contribution is also important and also needs investment. The staff are the practice's most valuable resource both in terms of what they cost to employ and, more importantly, what they contribute to supporting the practice infrastructure. Effective and efficient staff do not just develop on their own - the partnership will need to invest to allow the practice to deliver its service to today's expected high standards.

### Sources of funding

This is a messy area, probably because bureaucracy has not kept pace with the rapid changes that have taken place in primary care during the past five years.

Most leaders in the NHS would agree that multidisciplinary, multiprofessional training is a good thing, to move staff towards better understanding and trust, and the vision of a seamless service for patients. However, funding for the practice team's training comes from a variety of sources, making access tricky but not impossible. The first place to look for the information you need will be your Health Authority. Each Authority in the country will have different policies in this area.

*Non-fundholding practices*
A rule of thumb is that all the practice's employed staff (i.e. administration staff, practice nurses and the practice manager) will have access to the GMS training budget. Attached staff (such as district nurses and health visitors) have access through their managers to Working Paper 10 funding. GPs have postgraduate education allowance (PGEA); points towards this allowance can be gathered for in-house training at the discretion of the GP tutor at your postgraduate centre.

*Fundholding practices*
GP fundholders have staff training allocations within their budgets. It is possible to identify this amount and ring-fence it strictly. It is also possible that your Health Authority has primary-care development funding that you may be able to bid for. As from April 1996, fundholding practices can use their savings for training.

*Other sources*
Other sources of funding could be via pharmaceutical companies, but this would have to be in line with the practice policy on sponsorship.

# Chapter Two

## Training needs analysis

# Training needs analysis

**H**aving come this far in securing an infrastructure for a team training strategy that has the team's support, the next step is to identify what people want and need that will enhance their learning and that matches well with the practice's agenda. The choices people make will also need to match the practice budget. There are various ways of obtaining this data. The secret here is to find a way that suits your practice in terms of its size and what it wants to achieve.

Two options are:

1. Individual interviews
2. A group exercise

## Individual training interviews

If it is decided that there will be personal development plans for all the staff, then a formal interview with each member of the team will need to take place. A formal interview can be linked to appraisal or job review, or can stand alone as an interview to help the practice and its team members be really clear about what the needs are.

At these interviews, each team member will have the opportunity to express his/her development needs and aspirations. It is also an opportunity for the practice to explain to everyone what it is trying to achieve in broad terms. The vehicle for this would be your health needs assessment, if the practice is fundholding; or the business or practice plan that describes the practice's current state, its vision for the future and the strategy to get there.

All plans must take into account external factors, such as changes in government or in policy. Practice plans do have to be flexible and continually reviewed against factors over which they have no control. It is far better to be proactive and responsive than reactive and repressed. It is about defining the desired outcomes for the practice and measuring progress against that. A practice plan may well contain decisions such as to change the way the nursing care is delivered by taking a team approach; that is, district nurses, health visitors and practice nurses offering a more integrated service to patients so that professional boundaries are altered to accommodate patient needs more fully. Or to be fully computerised within the year, including all consultations and appointments. These kinds of decisions will have major implications for staff in terms of their skills and knowledge levels; their attitudes to change may well be the biggest hurdle for some individuals to get over.

Interviews with the staff will be a time to discuss the plan, highlighting the benefits to patients and the implications for each team member, and to outline what is expected from them that will contribute to the team plan. These interviews will need to be sensitively handled. People have a fear of change and can feel threatened by it. To overcome fear, people need to understand the benefits of the proposed change, feel consulted and supported, and be able to influence the change themselves. Any opposition to the change needs to be minimised, before the change can be successful.

## Preparation

Organise the training interviews so that they are allocated as much time as possible. It would be helpful to circulate to staff a copy of the practice plan if there is one. The plan will describe the longer-term vision, underpinned by clear goals and objectives for the practice and a strategy for achieving these, including targets and short-term milestones. Such a plan needs to be decided by the partnership, and will be even more useful if the team has contributed to it. It will make the task of joint training plans so much easier.

It would also be useful to give people a copy of the kind of questions you will be asking at the interview, to give them some time to prepare. You know the staff, so your own questions are probably the best. The aim here is to get people to relate their experience accurately and honestly; for them to share with you their desires and aspirations; for them to be able to say what they find difficult, what they may need help with. It is a time for you to recognise and acknowledge their contribution to the practice and how you see their role developing in the future.

## Sample preparation questions

- What knowledge and skills do I have already to do my job? (This is the baseline data for you to review progress against.)
- What knowledge and skills do I need to do my job?
- What will I want to know and be able to do for my job in the future?
- What knowledge and skills do I want that would give me the most job satisfaction?
- Which parts of my job do I do really well?
- Which parts of my job do I find most difficult, and why?
- Are there any factors that prevent me doing my job to my satisfaction?
- What other concerns do I have?
- Do I have knowledge and skills which I would be able to share with other members of the team, that would help them in their jobs?

## Conducting the interviews

These kinds of questions will elicit some very rich data, so it will be worth setting the interviews up well. This will mean spending time acknowledging each individual, thanking them for their time, saying you know how busy they are, showing you are really interested in what they are about to say. If you create a rapport in this way, the interview will be a good experience for you both. There may be some negotiation between you as to what may be possible and what may not; it is important not to make any promises at this stage. Keep a record of the outcome for each individual. The interview should end with you saying what will happen next. This will be something along the lines of, when you have interviewed everyone you will analyse and prioritise all the data, and draw up a written plan that will identify the resources allocated to meeting the team's training and development needs.

This plan will need to include defined outcomes for your training investment - for the individual, the practice and the patients. This is so that you have a measurement by which to evaluate the critical success factors of the training strategy and can be aware of what is outstanding, what is holding up progress, or where you may have got stuck. The resources specified will be the budget and the staff allocated to training and development. It does need to be clear that this plan will be reviewed at least annually, or whenever the practice changes direction.

### After the interviews

From the notes you have made at the interviews, you will be able to identify the common ground between team members' needs and the needs of the practice to improve and develop service delivery. In relation to your defined budget, you can work out the best way of delivering these needs. Some of these may be met by co-ordinating in-house programmes, particularly when the need is universal and supports the practice infrastructure. Training programmes on subjects such as communication skills, assertiveness, team development, medical law, information technology and audit, may be useful for most members of the team. For more specialised clinical knowledge, for example in chronic diseases, it may be better to send individual team members to an external programme. Management skills are recognised as a development need by increasing numbers of practices. External management courses are costly, so you may have to prioritise. You can use your practice plan to help you do this. The interviews will have helped you to identify in-house 'experts' in some of the areas you want help with. You may wish to develop your potential trainers - and that could include you.

Cost a plan to match your budget allocation, taking into account as far as possible the needs of the individuals and the needs of the practice. You will not please everyone, so it might be helpful to say what could be rolled over into next year's plan.

Map out the training plan, at least provisionally, in much the same way as a holiday planner (any training plan will of course have to relate to the team members' holiday plans). Training plans will coincide with the academic year starting in September/October, which is when most external courses and programmes begin. Working out release for training and service cover presents the same nightmares as holiday planning, but it is all part of the management task. It will require tactful negotiation on your part, and a commitment to the plan on the part of the team to make this a smooth operation. This is why it is so important to ensure team ownership by a bottom-up approach to the training strategy as described earlier. Whatever your investment in time and energy was then, the payoff comes now. The team are more likely to co-operate at this point having had a say at the beginning.

## Training needs identified by a group

The team members may decide that they would like to start with an in-house training programme. Identifying the group's needs together has many advantages. People are more likely to be committed to the learning they choose for themselves. Those team members most resistant to training will appreciate having a say in what will happen; they are more likely to attend and co-operate, particularly when they see other people being enthusiastic about in-house training. It is unlikely that they will want to be left out or left behind.

### The process

You should try to arrange a meeting at a time when most staff can come. Start by reminding the team of the aims of the practice training plan; check their expectations from the meeting; address their concerns and answer any questions.

It might be a good idea for the team to set some ground rules to create the climate for the meeting. They increase the level of safety, and put in the boundaries for working. A few to get started might be:

- Agree the time available.
- This is a team meeting.
- Everyone will have the opportunity to speak.

People do not always know what they need straight away, so it may be helpful if you produce a list of suggestions to help the process. Such a list might include:

- Medical law.

- Health and safety.

- Information technology.

- Medical audit.

- Communication skills, to include
  - assertiveness
  - managing difficult people and situations
  - the practice complaints procedure
  - telephone communications.

- Practice finance (how the practice earns its income).

- Practice administration and procedures.

Next, go through each topic on the list explaining what it will involve and who might be good to teach it. At this point, you could ask the team to form pairs to discuss the list, and identify any topics that might be missing from it. Allow about 10 minutes for this, and make sure that they know that they do not have to agree.

Begin the feedback by identifying any missing topics that the team members perceive as a need. Include these in the list. Then ask each individual to list his/her own priorities. One way to handle this would be to take a vote on each topic, with the number of votes determining the priority. Six or seven might be a suitable number of topics to start the programme with. It is very important that it is the group's choice that takes priority and not your perception of what is important.

Next you need to determine together the length of the programme (number of weeks, months etc.), the length of each session, the best day of the week, the best time of day. You may choose to have a two-hour session once a week over a lunch time for six weeks, or for the sessions to be in the evening. You may be able to have a half-day training for half of the staff while the other half covers the work, then the reverse. For example, the afternoon staff could have a morning's training while the morning staff cover, then the morning staff have the afternoon training while the afternoon staff do the shift. There are many solutions to this time problem; you and the team need to find the right one for you.

## New recruits

The importance of induction training for new recruits must not be overlooked. So often the new staff member is seen as an immediate asset to the practice, able to fill the gap and be effective from day one. The 'thrown in at the deep end' learning method has been popular in the past, and still operates today in some practices. The staff are too important and valuable to the practice not to have that value recognised by a good induction programme. Giving an excellent start to a new job is much easier than having to put right mistakes and oversights later on. There are no set rules for this. The content, method, time period and person leading the induction process will be determined by the structure of the practice and the responsibilities of the particular job. The purpose of induction, however, is general[2]:

- To help obtain the best possible performance from the new employee in the shortest time practicable.
- To give the new team member an understanding of the practice's main purpose, to provide the context within which the job operates.
- To make the new team member aware of the roles of other team members.
- To identify immediate and longer-term training and development needs.

However confident a new team member might be, and however well qualified, there will always be a gap between what experience and skills s/he arrives with and what the practice expects from him/her. The sooner this gap is identified and the training implemented, the sooner the practice will have full value for the investment in recruiting that member of staff. For staff such as receptionists, where there is more than one post in the practice, an induction programme can be adapted and used whenever a new receptionist starts work.

# Chapter Three

## Planning the training

# Planning the training

## Organising training events

Having designed the programme with the team, it is important to start with the most popular choices and leave out the least popular for the time being. Then ask yourself, in the light of the team's comments, if you were to run a training session on this topic what would you want to achieve by it - be very specific. This information will allow you to measure, at the evaluation stage, to what extent the event has been successful. It is also important to know what you want as an outcome, so that you can communicate that information to any potential trainers you have in mind.

Having made the decisions on content, you need to decide who you want to lead the course. The Health Authority usually has a list of preferred trainers in different areas of expertise. Any trainers you approach should request a meeting with you to help identify exactly what you want. They will then send you a proposal to match your team's needs; this will include their cost and expenses. It might be a good idea to see several trainers and select the one that you think will be the best match for your team. You can then arrange a programme at the dates and times selected by the team, and check trainer availability. Don't forget to request PGEA approval if applicable. When you send out the programme, include a return slip so you know exactly who is coming. The number of participants on any one programme should not exceed 20, or preferably 16. For information technology sessions, smaller numbers are advisable, particularly if it is a practical programme.

The next step is to find a suitable venue. A room in the practice is fine, but you may need to book the space well in advance. If there is no suitable room available, then you will need to book somewhere locally. This does not have to be expensive; providing the room is clean and warm with kitchen facilities, it will be suitable. You could consider community and civic buildings, village halls and postgraduate centres.

When costing the programme, include the venue, trainers, catering and equipment. Make sure the total is sensible and well within your budget allocation. Next confirm the numbers, with a list of names of those attending to the venue, any catering service, and the course trainer. Then find out from the trainer how s/he would like the room arranged, what equipment s/he will need and whether s/he wants to send any background material to the participants before the programme starts.

At the session, you may need a register of attendance for your records and possibly to claim funding reimbursement. Each participant will need an evaluation form; GPs may need one to send to the GP tutor for PGEA approval. After the programme is completed, invoices should be paid on receipt. The evaluations should be recorded, and a copy sent with a letter to the trainer. A summary of this administration procedure is given in Appendix 2 as a useful checklist.

# Training resources

We discussed funding for training in an earlier chapter. Now I would like to give some attention to the resources required to deliver training successfully.

### Training environment

*The venue*
Whatever you choose, it is important that it is comfortable for the number of people attending. Too big, and the group will have difficulty becoming cohesive with each other and with the trainer. Too small, and people's space will be invaded making learning less easy. There will need to be a kitchen, with provision for tea and coffee, and you will have to consider toilet facilities for the numbers attending. You will also need to be aware of the fire precautions.

*The environment*
Arrange the chairs in a way that is conducive to what is being taught.

Most professional trainers will say how they want the room arranged. Chairs in straight rows are fine for lectures, but not very useful for group participation. Chairs in a circle are useful for informal learning. Sometimes it is necessary to have tables. One large table can act as a barrier to the trainer/participant relationship; seating round several small tables is helpful if you are having lots of group work.

Heating/air conditioning must also be considered; it is important to get the learning environment right. Too hot or too cold are both very distracting and can hinder learning. You need to know how it works so that you can adjust it to suit your group.

It is also important to know how the lighting works and where the switches are, and to be able to adjust any other visual aids that might be used.

### Training equipment

If the practice is serious about organising team training, then there are a few basic investments to be made in equipment that will assist participants' learning. A flipchart, easel and pens would be a good start. This is helpful to give focus to the learning, by setting agendas, illustrating points, writing up group comments. It lends itself well to spontaneity. An overhead projector and screen are useful to illustrate a prepared talk, either by words, pictures or diagrams. Some people learn more easily when they can see examples.

Although expensive, a video and monitor are very useful to have. There are many training videos available covering most topics. These can be bought or hired. Most hospitals and universities have a teaching media department with libraries and catalogues to help you choose appropriately. Pharmaceutical companies often have videos that they will lend you free of charge; do review them first to make sure they reinforce the messages you want to give.

Before the 1990 GP contract changes and the NHS reforms contained in the White Paper *Working for Patients* in 1989, very little was written about primary care. Since that time, there have been many useful publications available covering all aspects of clinical care and organisational management. Some of these may be on your practice library shelves, or they can easily be borrowed from your hospital medical library.

Some publishing companies specialise in training materials. These are useful as they contain all aspects of the training process - both the content and methods of delivery. It is often possible to review these materials for a trial period just to see if they match the practice's philosophy.

## Training and learning options

Most of this book is concerned with in-house team learning. While this is certainly a useful strategy, it will not meet the learning needs of everyone. There are many other options for learning, some of which I will outline here.

Some members of the team may wish to obtain a formal qualification that fits in with the practice's plans. They need to choose wisely as these programmes are costly in terms of time, energy and money. It is important to gather as much information as possible; your Health Authority should be able to help here. They will know where appropriate programmes are being held, because they reimburse some of the cost to some practices. The reimbursement process should include quality control, so they should be able to tell you about standards.

For example, it might be decided that the new practice nurse should do an ENB (English Nursing Board) in basic nursing skills for practice nurses. Many colleges and universities offer such programmes. You should find the best programme on offer reasonably near to you. Universities are now offering programmes in health policy and social studies to degree level, some specialising in primary and community care. Send for the course listings from the universities near you. Part-time study to diploma and degree level has never been more accessible. You can contact the NHS Training Division, who have a national brokerage scheme and can assist you in finding an appropriate programme.

Distance learning through a correspondence course may suit some people. It is not necessary to give up much work time, but the discipline of working alone without the stimulus of a learning group can be really tough for some people.

There are many ways to learn in groups. Self-help groups, which meet regularly to share successes, identify difficulties and get new thinking, can be a very productive and safe way to learn. Coaching on a one-to-one basis, for example doing a job and discussing the outcome with a supervisor to identify the learning points, is a quick and productive way to learn. Temporary 'acting up' can be another useful way of giving team members a chance to develop. It has much the same advantages as job rotation, job exchange or job shadowing. The more team members understand each others' contributions, the more cohesive the team becomes and the more able they are to meet new challenges.

Training others is one way of learning. Firstly, there is what the learner will teach you. Secondly, the research and reading you will do around your subject to present it to the required level of knowledge and understanding is refining your own learning in a particular area. Asking team members to research projects, write reports, write up procedures, and develop handbooks and guidelines for others to read are all learning options. Most of us learn by trial and error; we have done this since birth. If something is not working, then we naturally try something else.

A summary of learning options is given in Appendix 3.

# Chapter Four

Be your own trainer/facilitator

# Be your own trainer/facilitator

The idea of being the trainer/facilitator for some of your in-house sessions may appeal to you. Certainly the cost of the training would be less, and you can be sure that procedures and processes will be taught in a way that reflects the practice's policy. However, unless you like leading and teaching, and you think you would enjoy enabling others to learn, perhaps this is not for you. Successful teachers are not always those who know the most about their subject.

## Principles of learning

### Things that help or hinder learning

Take a moment to recall the times when you were in a learning setting; this does not have to be in school. Try to recall a time when the learning went well. Remember what were the attributes that made it such a good experience and helped you to learn. Make a list of them. Remember next a time when the learning was tough or difficult; make a list of those attributes that hindered your learning. You may notice from your list of positive and negative attributes that many are directly related to your teachers. I have provided sample lists in Table 1, but it is your experience that is important. This should help you to get a feel for the qualities and skills required to be a successful teacher, and decide if it is really for you.

| *Table 1.* Helping and hindering factors | |
|---|---|
| *Helps learning* | *Hinders learning* |
| An enthusiastic teacher | Being lectured at for hours |
| Group work | Being talked down to |
| Lots of examples | No time for questions Continued overleaf |

| | |
|---|---|
| Visual aids | Being put on the spot |
| Time to try out new things | Uncomfortable chairs |
| Lots of participation | Fear of examinations |
| Handouts | Irrelevant material |
| OK to make mistakes | When people rubbish you |

This is a typical list a group will give you when you ask these questions. It is helpful to do this at the beginning of any new training. This is because, like ground rules, it describes the climate in which people would like their learning to take place. If you can all agree to the helps and hinders, then they can be used to keep everyone on track. The teacher knows what is expected and what is not wanted from him/her. The group will have responsibility for saying when it is not right for them. The teacher can remind the group of the agreement should any-one not want to co-operate.

If you decide that you want to take on a trainer role, then you will need to know a bit about how people learn. We have just explored what people say helps them learn. You will notice that it is based on how it is experienced, how the pieces come together when people are given the chance to experiment, try out and discuss together. We all learn differently; we experience our world differently. Notice how small children learn; little children do not have to have all of the pieces, they just have what they have and are naturally curious about it. They will try something out; if it doesn't work, then they try something different. Imagine children climbing stairs, for example - they will just keep at it till they get to the top. However many times an adult might remove them, they will maintain curiosity and keep having another go. It is only when their natural curiosity is interfered with by some adult telling them they are stupid or clumsy that their most natural way of learning can be interrupted. Children have a knack of trusting what adults say, so can easily begin to have negative beliefs about themselves. This is often reinforced by the school system. The way we were taught in the classroom would not have been helpful for us all. So often we are told what it is that we do not do well. Positive criticism, being told what we do well, will encourage us to keep improving.

There are some general principles of learning which it may be helpful to understand as you approach learning to train:

- When learners find out for themselves, this aids learning.

- If learners set their own goals, by deciding what they want very specifically, learning is more likely to take place.

- When what learners want to learn is clear and relevant, more learning is possible.

- Awareness by the teacher and the learners of what gets in the learners' way, will help the learners to succeed.

- Learning is more likely when expectations are high.

- When it is safe enough to make mistakes, learning is more interesting.

- Time for reflection, regular review and checking of the learning method by the teacher and the learner, will enhance the learning.

- Starting the learning from where the learners are, building on what they know and the skills they have, will aid learning.

- Where the learners are actively involved, more learning is likely to take place.

If you were to apply these principles to yourself while learning to train, it may help you to make the learning a good experience.

**Stages of learning**

It may also be helpful to know that there are some stages that we go through when we are learning anything new. I will take the example of learning to drive a car to illustrate this.

Remember the time when you first sat in the driving seat of a car, looking at the controls, fiddling with the switches, feeling your feet on the pedals, sounding the horn. At that time you were unaware of what it was you did not know. This is stage one, called **unconscious incompetence.**

As we start to learn, have our first lesson, we suddenly become aware of how inexperienced we are, how complex driving is, and just how much we have to learn. This is often a difficult stage, and many of us are tempted to give up at this point unless well motivated. The motivation for a person to be able to drive is often high - freedom from parents, access to work, and many other opportunities. This stage is called **conscious incompetence**, when we become aware of how much we do not know.

The third stage is when we become aware that we are making progress. We have practised and experimented; we are beginning to acquire the knowledge and skills. We know how to do it, but we have to think hard and concentrate to keep it going. Can you recall all the complex processes to achieve a hill start? This stage involves making small, progressive steps as we become more skilled. This is called **conscious competence**, when we are aware that we are getting it right.

The final stage is **unconscious competence**. Do you remember driving to work today? Did you consciously have to concentrate at each hill, traffic-light or junction? A new sense has taken over - the kinaesthetic sense of unconscious movement or muscular effort. By repeatedly driving the car, we have arrived at a level of unconscious competence where the whole process seems natural and easy and doesn't require so much concentration.

This relatively simple model may help you learn to train well, by recognising that the stage which you are at is only a stage. With perseverance it will pass and you will soon be training with unconscious competence.

Explaining these stages of learning at the beginning of training events can also be encouraging to participants.

## Facilitating group learning

At this point it may be useful to think some more about 'how' to train; knowing the principles of learning is useful, but what is it you 'do' to facilitate a training event well? I define 'to facilitate' as 'to make easy', or 'to enable', so what are the skills and behaviours required to make learning easy that match the learning principles?

Think of a time that you really valued when you were in a learning group working through a task, or taking part in a discussion that was being led by a facilitator. What was it that made it work for you? What specifically did the leader do to assist the process? If you can't remember anything much at all, it could be that the leader was so skilled you didn't notice what s/he was doing; you just know it was a good learning experience, you were able to contribute and hear the views of others, and do the exercises to time without feeling rushed. These would be the signs of good facilitation. How is it achieved? Well, to make easy, is not itself easy, but the skills can be learnt so that it is possible to do it at the unconsciously competent level.

To be able to facilitate a learning group, the first responsibility is to build the climate to enable the group to work well. It will be useful to begin to notice your own state. By this I mean your thoughts, feelings, emotions, and physical and mental energy. What might be a good state for facilitation? It might be that you have to be genuinely wanting to help your group. You might define this as being yourself and showing a lively interest and concern for the group. You can do this by sharing any common purpose, any professional understanding or shared objectives you may have. If your current state of mind is not that resourceful, just thinking about your desired state will enable you to move some way towards it. Think of the times when you have been able to help others learn; recall very specifically what you did and how you felt. Have a picture of yourself in your mind's eye at a time when you did well. See yourself and notice the resources you had; it might be that you were enthusiastic, or you were very clear and stimulating. Enthusiasm is infectious, so being in that state yourself will infect your learners. Whatever you notice, bring these resources back into the present and you will have moved towards your desired state to facilitate learning.

Begin your learning session by introducing yourself, if you are not already well known to all the group; say enough about yourself to let people know you know what you are about. Then say what the aims for the session are. This could be about the learning or about how you want it to be for them. For example, you could say: "By the end of this session you will have a good understanding of the NHS reforms, and a chance to add your views. Some of this we will do by working in small groups". At the beginning of any learning session, it is very important for the individual group members to have a chance to speak. The level of safety goes up for people when they know who is in the room with them. So they all need to introduce themselves, to say something about themselves and their role, and what they want to learn from the session.

You could have some questions prepared on a flipchart to make the process easier:

- Name

- Role

- What do you want from this session?

Make a list on your flipchart of the participants' expectations. This helps the participants to think clearly about their own desired outcomes, and will enable you to get an idea of the knowledge level of the group so that you can pitch your material at the right level. Most importantly, the participants are setting their own agenda about what they specifically want to cover. This, in turn, will enable you to evaluate the session at the end; you can simply check out with the participants whether their goals have been met.

This first group exercise is useful to build up a learning climate. Even if the participants know each other, it is important to get them to speak about their expectations. There will be a lot of agreement and some surprises.

Earlier in this chapter I looked at what can help or hinder learning. This is the point at which to establish with the group what would help or hinder their learning. Begin by explaining the purpose of the exercise - that is, to decide together how you want the learning climate to be. Give some examples of what you mean.

Next, you could ask the group to get into pairs to do an exercise called 'talk and listen'. This means that one person talks about his/her learning experiences while the other pays attention and listens without interruption to what is said. The theory is that when people receive good attention they are able to sort out their thinking really well. The first person speaks for about five minutes, then they change over, remembering first to write down the first talker's key points. These are the points from their own experience, the times when they learnt well and noticed what made it work for them; then the points that made their learning difficult. Take the feedback from the pairs, one helping and one hindering point from each pair. Do this until there are none left. This gives everyone a chance to contribute to the list.

One way to do this is to divide a flipchart page with a line down the middle; put a heading of 'Helps' on one half and 'Hinders' on the other. Write up all the points. If confidentiality is not on the list, then it is important that you add it. This is because people learn better when they can use their own examples. People need to feel safe enough to do this, so an agreement about confidentiality within the group is essential. I define confidentiality to groups by saying that it is fine to discuss with people outside the group what you have learnt from the sessions - the outcome. What is not good is to discuss the process of how you got there - the content. I also agree confidentiality between the group and myself, so they know that what they say to me stays within the room.

If you can agree as a group to uphold the helps to learn factors and avoid the hinders, then you have a useful tool to keep everyone on track. You will know what the group expects from you. The group has responsibility for saying when it is not right for them. You can remind the group of this agreement should anyone not want to co-operate. Pin the chart up where it is easily seen by everyone - it is much easier for people to say when they are not happy with something if there is a visible agreement to refer to.

## Designing the session

The first step is to define the time available for the learning session, and then allocate time for introductions, ground rules, aims and expectations.

This should be followed by some information on the topic - some theory or model to help start off the learning process.

Most people's attention span is around 20 minutes. So you should aim for 20-30 minute chunks of information followed by an exercise that will either develop the group's thinking or give the opportunity to try out some of the models. A session of 90 minutes in total followed by a break is about right. Four chunks of 90 minutes throughout one day's training is ideal. An outline course design is provided as Appendix 4.

## Popular training procedures (exercises)

*Brainstorming*
This is a technique for extracting a great many ideas from a group in a short time. The group is given a topic, or a question, to focus upon. For a few minutes, members of the group say anything that occurs to them on that topic and a scribe writes the contributions up on a flipchart - anything that is said, however irrelevant, silly or challengeable. During that time there is no discussion, as the purpose is to produce ideas. Nothing is censored or evaluated during the brainstorm. At the end of the exercise, members have a chance to elaborate on their comments and to challenge and discuss all the ideas produced.

*Buzz groups*
These are designed to energise the group members after spells of inactivity. After listening to an input, members are asked to turn to their neighbour and share their views or impressions for a few minutes before asking questions. Another version is to have small discussion groups of four to six people who share their views with each other for five minutes. Brief reports from buzz groups can be brought back to a general session. This can be a useful guide as to what has been heard, understood, not grasped, or disagreed with.

*Case study*
This involves the use of detailed description of an event, a character, a situation or a problem. It can be real or contrived, and it is usually followed by a group discussion. The facilitator stays out of the group. At the end of the discussion, the facilitator draws out the learning from the reporting back session.

*Role-play*
This allows for skills practice or an exploration of ideas and feelings in a simulation of a real life experience. Individuals can be given the option to role play, as some people are uncomfortable with it. Start with volunteers who can choose or be given roles, which are then performed. The more spontaneous and less scripted, the more useful it is. However, individuals should be well briefed, and afterwards they should be 'de-roled' and the learning processed.

*Training groups*
One of the most effective ways of learning something can be by having to teach it to others. Groups can be asked to teach skills or present information to other groups. Besides clarifying for themselves what it is that they have to teach, they are required to design an exercise, demonstration or programme to 'teach' to the other group. This kind of activity can be very stimulating and entertaining.

# Group skills

When facilitating the group's learning it is helpful to consider two dimensions:

1. The task behaviours - that is the activity required to get the job done.

2. The people behaviours in the group.

As the trainer/facilitator, you have the responsibility to monitor and manage both of these. This is where your group skills become invaluable. Your skills are applied on the basis of a judgement of the group's needs at any given moment in the learning process.

**Task behaviours**

We begin a learning session by stating the purpose and clarifying what is going to happen. Next, it is important to check the level of the group's understanding. This you can do by asking about people's expectations, or asking them to talk about their experiences to-date. Sometimes, it is necessary to motivate a group to learn. This can be done by emphasising the benefits to the group and the individuals if the learning is achieved.

During learning sessions, there is a need for some theoretical input. This needs to be divided with group work to enable everyone to give their opinions and ideas. It is also the facilitator's job to make sure that the learning stays on course to achieve the aims of the session. Reviewing where the learning has got to, and summing up from time to time, will help you do this.

## People behaviours

At the same time as facilitating the learning, it is necessary to facilitate the participants' behaviours. This is done initially by listening and looking. It is useful to take a group's temperature from time to time; are they tense, bored, dominated by one or two people? Are they all taking part? Are there any sub-groups forming? Who exercises influence, and how? Then ask yourself what you need to do differently to change these behaviours into more useful ones. It could be that you need to be more empathic. Maybe give more encouragement and support by bringing in more reticent participants. You may need to defuse tension. When groups are stuck it can be useful to break into pairs and take feedback; invariably groups get new learning from this and can then move on. You should certainly intervene when you have been contracted to do so via the helps or hinders learning rules. A summary of group facilitation skills[3] is given in Appendix 5.

It is also important to know when not to intervene; certainly if what you do will not add to the quality of the learning, for example if your intervention would 'depower' the learner. I have seen this happen when the trainer/facilitator indulges his/her own needs by showing off his/her own cleverness or knowledge. This is easily done; I do it myself, but less and less as time passes. The trainer/facilitator's job is to allow the learners to get there at their own pace.

## Managing difficult behaviours

When people behave inappropriately during learning sessions, however difficult that is for you, remember that the behaviour is not the person; you must continue to respect the person whilst challenging the behaviour. To do this well you must pay attention to your own body language, and the tone of your voice, as well as the words you choose, when confronting difficult behaviour.

All these interventions will only work if they are carried out in a non-blaming way - that is, focusing on the issues not the person. Your body language and tone of voice have to reinforce the non-blaming message. Certainly, this is not always easy. Remember the stages of learning; if you make a mistake, it's only a stage. Reflect afterwards on what you did, decide what could have been better, and try that next time. With time and practice, you will be facilitating learning effortlessly, which can

**Table 2.** Common types of difficult behaviour, and possible solutions

| Difficult behaviour | Possible solution |
|---|---|
| **Distracting** - asks questions, makes comments off the point. No apparent understanding. | Confront. Invite to talk to you at the break. Check out understanding. Invite other points of view from other members. |
| **Complaining** - continually finds fault with all aspects of the training. Shows dissatisfaction by indirect expression of negative feeling such as moaning and groaning. | Ignore complaints. Avoid giving power. Confront negativity by asking for feedback at the end of the training. Suggest suspending judgement and evaluate the material later. You may question their presence at the training. |
| **Fighting** - disagrees; asks leading questions: "Don't you think . . .". Seeks power and control. | Build on their knowledge, not their hostility. Invite them to elaborate on their 'ideas'. Confront leading questions straight away: "You sound irritated to me, is there something bothering you?" Thank them for their views. |

Continued overleaf

| | |
|---|---|
| **Knowing it all** - expert on everything. Adds to or corrects others. Takes expert power. Looking for control. | Avoid getting into an argument. Invite them to present an opposing point of view. Question why they are in the training. Thank them for information. |
| **Monopolising** - takes up attention; others withdraw. Poor listening skills. Long-winded interruptions. | Invite others to contribute. Encourage person to listen. Get listeners in the group to speak more and speakers to listen more. Suggest they give others a chance to speak. |
| **Withdrawing** - sits quietly, looking miserable, pained, blank, disgusted. Negative non-verbal behaviour. | Encourage them to express their feelings verbally. Be non-critical. Talk directly: "Is there something about what we are doing that does not interest you?". Share your perception of their non-verbal signals and invite explanation. Encourage them to give their point of view to possibly influence what is happening. |
| **Projecting** - attributes their own feelings to others: "I don't think anyone understands this". Speaking for others. | Direct talk: "Are you speaking for yourself? I'm wondering if that is really the way *you* feel."; "Let's check out that other people are really experiencing what you attribute to them". |

be very satisfying for you. The benefits to the team will be noticeable; they will become more cohesive in the way they deliver services to patients. This can only enhance patients' experience of the care offered by the practice.

# Chapter Five

## Making the most of feedback

# Making the most of feedback

The need to reflect and review all management tasks in the practice is very important, but none more so than the management of the people. This includes their training and development. If you make this investment in a team training strategy, then you need to know its value. The value can be measured in terms of what it cost financially, against the gains in individuals' development, the practice's progress against its plan and the quality of the service to patients. This is why it is so important to have defined your desired outcomes at the outset.

The three main areas to consider are:

- Assessing
- Costing
- Evaluating

## Assessing

It is standard practice for formal training sessions and courses to be assessed as they progress. This is usually done at the end of a particular session, and at the end of a programme of sessions. It is done by the individuals or by the whole group together. The process can be either oral or written, or both. The purpose is to provide immediate feedback to trainers and co-ordinators alike, for them to be able to measure if they are on track. Are they meeting the participants' needs at an intellectual and practical level? An assessment will gather information in the following areas for it to be immediately useful and allow for modifications to be made:

- Did the session/course meet the aims and expectations of the participants?
- What did participants find of particular value?

49

- What could have been better or different?

- Was the material offered at a level that was accessible for participants - not too advanced, or too basic?

- Was the pace of the course too fast, too slow or just right?

- Was the course too long, of satisfactory length or too short?

- Was any topic covered that did not seem relevant to the course?

- Were there any topic areas left out?

It is not always necessary to ask all of these questions, it will depend on the training offered. A training assessment form is usually designed to match the particular training session; an example is given in Appendix 6. The questions asked will also depend on who is to use the information. This could include:

- Participants, who will gain an early impression of the usefulness of the new learning to them.

- The practice, who will need immediate feedback on the investment.

- Health Authorities, who reimburse funding, and will want to know to what extent the training has been successful and what changes in their strategy they may need to make.

- Trainers/facilitators, who will want to know how successful they were and where they may need to make changes.

## Costing

We discussed in an earlier chapter the importance of setting an annual budget for training. This, of course, means keeping track year on year of the costs involved.

In addition to the cost of training fees, there is also the expense of materials, transport and accommodation. If staff have to cover for absent team members then there is overtime or time off in lieu to be calculated. If there are team members attending outside courses, one way of increasing the return on this investment is to have them report back to the practice on completion of the course. This could take the form of a short written report or a talk at a practice meeting. Feedback given in this way allows more people to benefit from the cost of the training. It is also a sign to the team of the value the practice places on the importance of learning.

The cost of in-house training needs to be calculated and monitored. The fees of outside speakers/trainers/facilitators are obvious costs, but not so straightforward are the rates of pay of staff receiving training plus the planning costs, materials and administration.

It is important to cost training in terms of its value for money. It can also be useful to let staff know what these costs are, as this sends out the message to the team how highly they are valued by the practice.

# Evaluating

Evaluation is making a judgement about the **value** of something. In this case, it means measuring the effectiveness of the training strategy itself, and of the training delivered within it.

This will mean going back to the original aims and objectives for the team training strategy, and reviewing with the team to what extent these have been achieved. Review task outcomes against your indicators:

- What changes in practice can you identify?
- Any increases in knowledge?
- Improved standards?
- Changes in patients' behaviour?
- Process outcomes, i.e. changes in team effectiveness or relationships?
- Individual outcomes, i.e. development of skills, changes in attitude and levels of confidence?

It is also important to measure the value of the work to you as the manager of it, the champion who made it happen. Having a sense of the benefits at a professional and personal level will be a motivation for you to continue. Being aware of the pitfalls and difficulties will allow you to be on a path of continuous improvement

Any employer or manager of people has a responsibility to identify training needs and meet them, as well as to evaluate the effectiveness of the training delivered. Organisations do not survive without people who are confident and competent in what they do. When is this more important than in organisations that deliver health care to patients? If the trust people have in their professional health care is to be upheld, investment in the people who work within it has never been more important.

# References &
# Further Reading

# REFERENCES

1. Spiegal N, Murphy EA, Kinmonth AL, Ross F, Bain DJB, Coates R. Managing change in general practice: a step by step guide. *Br Med J* 1992; **304**: 231-4.

2. Irvine S, Haman H. *Making sense of personnel management.* Radcliffe Medical Press, 1993.

3. Health Education Authority. *Manual for use with primary healthcare teams,* 1994.

# FURTHER READING

Dean J. *Making sense of practice finance.* Radcliffe Medical Press, 1994.

Drury M. *The new practice manager* (2nd edn). Radcliffe Medical Press, 1992.

Ellis N, Chisholm J. *Making sense of the Red Book* (2nd edn). Radcliffe Medical Press, 1993.

Ellis N. *Making sense of general practice.* Radcliffe Medical Press, 1994.

Grabinar J. *The really useful handbook for the practice receptionist.* Publishing Initiatives Books, 1996.

Hasler J, Bryceland C, Hobden Clarke L, Rose P. *Handbook of practice management.* Churchill Livingstone, 1993.

Havelock P. *Communication skills and teamworking in primary care.* Publishing Initiatives Books, 1995.

Jones T. *The structure of the National Health Service* (2nd edn). Publishing Initiatives Books, 1997.

Pickersgill R. *The law and general practice.* Radcliffe Medical Press, 1993.

Pritchard P, Pritchard J. *Teamwork for primary and shared care. A practical workbook.* Oxford Medical Publications, 1994.

Tettersell M, Sawyer J, Salisbury C. *Handbook of practice nursing.* Churchill Livingstone, 1992.

# Appendices

# Appendix 1

## Domainal map

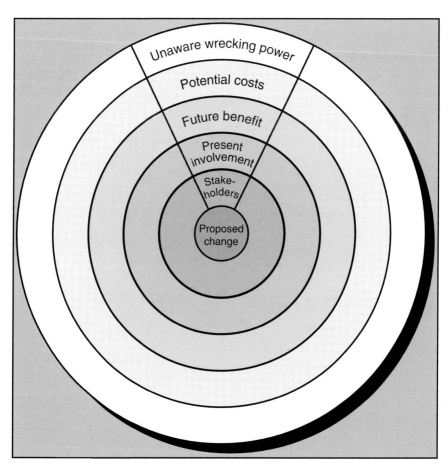

*Reproduced with permission from the BMJ Publishing Group.*

# Appendix 2

## Administration checklist for organising training

- Decide on course to be run.
- Arrange on a date when most people can come.
- Decide who will lead on the course: speaker/trainer/facilitator.
- Find venue.
- PGEA approval application (if applicable).
- Advertise the event.
- Record take up.
- Joining instructions for participants.
- Confirm numbers to venue, caterer.
- Hire any equipment required.
- Send course leader list of participants and a map to find venue.
- Preparation on the day: registers, name badges, catering arrangements.
- Assessment forms.
- Send assessments to course leaders.
- Reports to GP tutor, if applicable.

# Appendix 3

## List of learning options

- Attending a college or university to gain a qualification.
- Learning sets.
- Short courses (maximum five days).
- Job instruction - one-to-one training; on the job training.
- Coaching - doing a job and discussing the outcome with a supervisor.
- Distance learning programmes.
- In-house training.
- Published training materials for specific topics.
- Training others.
- Job rotation.
- Job exchange.
- Job shadowing.
- Re-defining a job description to add challenge.
- Visits to other establishments.
- Attending meetings.
- Writing reports.
- Reading books and journals.
- Watching a video.
- Projects.
- Temporary acting up.

# Appendix 4

## Practice team communications workshop
### – Outline course design

| | |
|---|---|
| *1.30* | Welcome |
| | Introductions |
| | Outline of workshop |
| | Aims and expectations |
| | How we learn |
| *2.00* | Assessing our relationships with self and others |
| | How to get rapport and maintain it |
| *3.15* | Tea |
| *3.30* | Do we get the response we deserve? |
| *4.15* | Dealing with difficult people |
| *4.45* | Questions |
| | Assessment |
| *5.00* | Home |

# Appendix 5

## Group facilitation skills

| Task behaviours | People behaviours |
|---|---|
| Clarifying the task | Listening |
| Checking understanding | Bringing in participants |
| Motivating to the task | Showing empathy |
| Seeking opinions and ideas | Validating, giving recognition |
| Monitoring direction | Giving encouragement and support |
| Processing the learning | Defusing tension |
| Delegating task leadership | Checking feelings |
| Giving task feedback | Expressing feelings |
| Reviewing | Confronting behaviours |
| Summarising | Reviewing and processing |

# Appendix 6

## Practice team communications workshop
## – *Assessment form*

*A.* What did you find of value to you?

---

*B.* What would you have liked to have been different?

---

*C.* On a score from 1 to 5 (1 = poor to 5 = excellent), how would you rate this workshop?

Please tick your choice:

1 ☐     2 ☐     3 ☐     4 ☐     5 ☐

# Index